# *A Matter of Taste* 〈Intro〉

## 健康生活に見る食育と栄養〈入門編〉

by

*Akiko Tsuda*
*Chris Valvona*
*Takako Yamato*
*Ayano Valvona*

NAN'UN-DO

***A Matter of Taste*** **〈Intro〉**



*Akiko Tsuda*
*Chris Valvona*
*Takako Yamato*
*Ayano Valvona*



Download Audio

音声ファイル
無料 DL
のご案内

このテキストの音声を無料で視聴（ストリーミング）・ダウンロードできます。自習用音声としてご活用ください。
以下のサイトにアクセスしてテキスト番号で検索してください。

**https://nanun-do.com**　テキスト番号［**512014**］

※ 無線 LAN（WiFi）に接続してのご利用を推奨いたします。

※ 音声ダウンロードは Zip ファイルでの提供になります。
お使いの機器によっては別途ソフトウェア（アプリケーション）の導入が必要となります。

# はじめに

本書は、前著『健康生活に見る食育と健康：A Matter of Taste』の入門編として、最新の栄養や食、健康に関する情報を盛り込んだ総合的な英語教材です。専門用語がわからなくても楽しめるよう、日本人英語教員（津田晶子、ヴァルヴォーナ綾乃）、イギリス人英語教員（Chris Valvona）、管理栄養士（大和孝子）が協力しながら制作しました。
各ユニットの構成は以下のとおりです。

### 考えてみましょう

この章の話題についてあらかじめ考えておきましょう。

### A *Vocabulary Check*

Reading Passage の中で、とくに重要な単語や未習だと思われる単語を取り上げました。定義が確認できたら、今度は音声で確認してみましょう。

### B *Dictation*

本文の中から穴埋めディクテーション用の問題を用意しました。ペアやグループで確認しても良いでしょう。

### Reading Passage

速読したり、一文ずつ精読したり、音読したりとさまざまなアプローチをしてみてください。Timed Reading で 1 分間にどれだけ読めたか、巻末の記録表に記録を取っておくと良いでしょう。

### C *Scan the Text*

スキャニングの練習です。本文から重要な表現を拾い読みしてみましょう。

### D *Reading Comprehension* E *Read and Think*

内容が理解できているか、確認します。

### F Useful Expressions

Reading Passage の中から役に立つ表現を選びました。和訳しましょう。

### G Over to You

章のまとめとして、学んだことを応用しながら自分の考えをまとめます。ペアやグループで考えてみても良いでしょう。

### Tea Break

食と栄養に関するクイズや映画情報などを紹介しました。発展的な学習として取り組んでください。

英語学習を通じて、健康的な食生活や多様な食文化に興味を持っていただくことが私たちの願いです。

最後に、本書の構想から出版に至るまで丸小雅臣氏、伊藤宏実氏をはじめとして南雲堂のスタッフの皆様にはたいへんお世話になりました。また、岩本弓子先生、Kelly MacDonald 先生には、テキスト制作時にご協力いただきました。心より感謝の意を表します。

著者一同

# Contents

UNIT 1

# エネルギー産生栄養素

# *Energy-Providing Nutrients*

## 考えてみましょう

あなたは栄養素について、どのくらい知っていますか？　知っていることを書き出してみましょう。

〈メモ〉

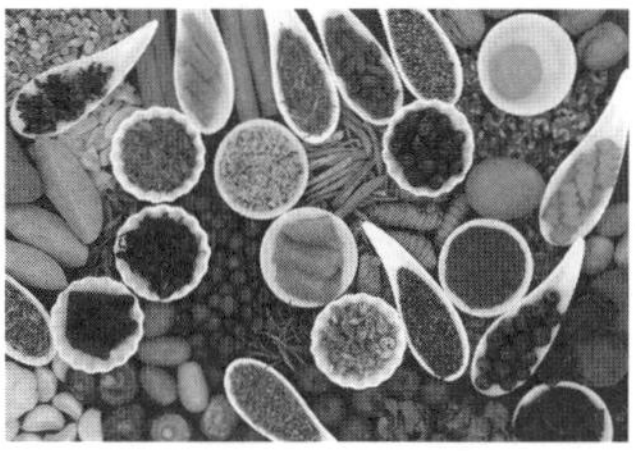

Nutrients: What we need to live

## A *Vocabulary Check* 2

次の日本語の意味を表す英語を下の語群から選び、(　　　) 内に書き出しなさい。また、音声を聴いてそれぞれの単語を発音しなさい。

1. 炭水化物　(　　　　　　　　　　　　　　)
2. 脂質　　　(　　　　　　　　　　　　　　)
3. 栄養素　　(　　　　　　　　　　　　　　)
4. 腎臓　　　(　　　　　　　　　　　　　　)
5. 脳　　　　(　　　　　　　　　　　　　　)

語群

kidney　　carbohydrates　　nutrient　　fats　　brain

## B *Dictation* 3

次の英文を聴き、＿＿＿に適切な語句を記入しなさい。

Your body needs proteins in order to [1] ___________ and to [2] ___________ cells and tissues. Your muscles, nails, [3] ___________, bones, organs, and [4] ___________ are all mostly [5] ___________ up of proteins.

# Reading Passage 4

[1] We need nutrients to live. "Energy-Providing Nutrients" are **proteins**, **carbohydrates**, and **fats**. Understanding what these "energy-providing nutrients" do, and what foods contain them, will help you keep a healthy, balanced diet and body.

## Proteins

[2] Your body needs proteins in order to grow and to repair cells and tissues. Your muscles, nails, skin, bones, organs, and hair are all mostly made up of proteins. You can find protein in meats, fish, tofu and other soy products, eggs, and dairy products such as milk and cheese.

## Carbohydrates

[3] Carbohydrates are the body's main source of energy. They are found in foods such as rice, noodles, bread, pasta, beans, potatoes, bran, and cereals. It is very important to get enough carbohydrates in your diet, because carbohydrates are turned into glucose in the body, and this is the energy source for your brain, red blood cells, and kidneys. However, if you have too many carbohydrates, they are turned into fat, which can lead to weight gain and other diet-related problems.

## Fats

[4] Fats are another source of energy. They are found in foods such as milk, cheese, butter, eggs, meat, oily fish, and nuts. Fats are important for many things, including healthy skin and hair, regular body temperature, and healthy cell function. Like carbohydrates, you should be careful not to consume too much fat in order to avoid unhealthy weight gain. Also, fats can be categorized into saturated fats and unsaturated fats. The unsaturated fats (found in olive oil, and oily fishes such as eel, mackerel, and tuna) can lower cholesterol and have other positive effects, so you don't need to avoid these.

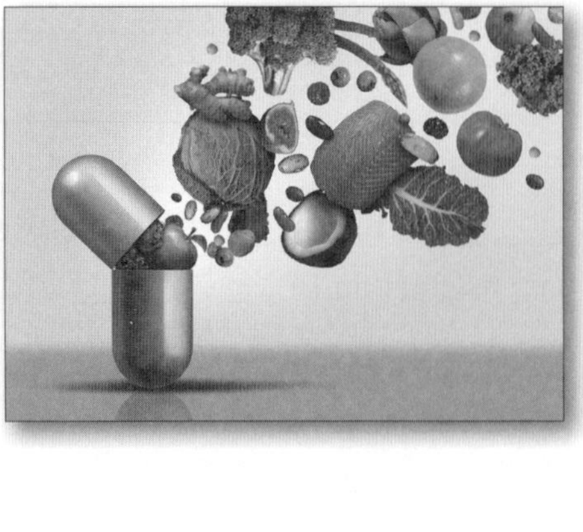

(267 words)

| | | | |
|---|---|---|---|
| Speed Reading | 1st time | ( | /wpm) |
| Speed Reading | 2nd time | ( | /wpm) |

## C *Scan the Text*

**1-5 の日本語の語句と同じ意味の英語の表現を a-e から選び、(　　　　) に記入しましょう。また、本文をよく読み、それらの表現に下線を引きましょう。**

1. (栄養) バランスのとれた食生活 (　　　　　　　　　　)
2. グルコースに変わる (　　　　　　　　　　)
3. 赤血球 (　　　　　　　　　　)
4. 体温 (　　　　　　　　　　)
5. 体重の増加 (　　　　　　　　　　)

a. balanced diet
b. body temperature
c. turn into glucose
d. weight gain
e. red blood cell

## D *Reading Comprehension*

**本文をよく読んで、正しければ T、間違っていれば F に○をつけましょう。**

1. To keep healthy, you need to consume energy-providing nutrients. **(T / F)**
2. Saturated fats can control cholesterol. **(T / F)**

## E *Read and Think*

**本文をよく読んで、それぞれの栄養素を多く含んでいる食品を書き出しましょう。**

①たんぱく質

---

②炭水化物

---

③脂質

---

## F Useful Expressions（～like）

**下線部に注意して、和訳しましょう。**

1. Like carbohydrates, you should be careful not to consume too much fat in order to avoid unhealthy weight gain.

------------------------------------------------------------

2. TV cooking shows are very popular in the UK, like in Japan.

------------------------------------------------------------

## G Over to You

**今日の昼食（または昨日の夕食）で食べたものを書き出し、たんぱく質、炭水化物、脂質に分けてみましょう。**

| | |
|---|---|
| **たんぱく質** | |
| **炭水化物** | |
| **脂質** | |

### Tea Break

**知っていますか？**

塩分の摂り過ぎは、高血圧症や胃がんのリスクが高まるといわれています。摂り過ぎには注意しましょう。1日の目標量：18歳以上（男性：8g未満、女性：7g未満）

出典：日本人の食事摂取基準2015年版

クイズ：塩分の最も多い食べ物はどれでしょうか？

A　アジの開き（100グラム）

B　カップラーメン（1個）

C　フライドポテトLサイズ（170グラム）

UNIT 2

栄養学：略史

# Nutrition Science: A Brief History

## 考えてみましょう

私たちにとって「栄養学」を学ぶことはどんなことに役に立つでしょうか？　考えてみましょう。

〈メモ〉

A serious field of research

## A Vocabulary Check 5

**次の日本語の意味を表す英語を下の語群から選び、(　　　) 内に書き出しなさい。また、音声を聴いてそれぞれの単語を発音しなさい。**

1. 糖尿病　(　　　　　　　　　　　　　　　)
2. ナトリウム　(　　　　　　　　　　　　　　　)
3. ビタミン　(　　　　　　　　　　　　　　　)
4. (病的な) 肥満　(　　　　　　　　　　　　　　　)
5. 添加物　(　　　　　　　　　　　　　　　)

語群

obesity　diabetes　additive　vitamin　sodium

## B Dictation 6

**次の英文を聴き、______ に適切な語句を記入しなさい。**

People have been interested in the [1] ___________ of food on their health for [2] ___________ years. As a result, nutrition science has [3] ___________ into a [4] ___________ field of [5] ___________.

# Reading Passage 7

[1] People have been interested in the effects of food on their health for many years. As a result, nutrition science has developed into a serious field of research. Here, we look at some big changes in the field over the years.

[2] In the 18th century, while at sea, many sailors got very sick and died from a disease called scurvy. An experiment in 1747 by Dr. James Lind found that eating limes prevented the disease. They didn't know it at the time, but the magic ingredient was a vitamin: vitamin C. However, vitamins were actually only 'discovered' in the first half of the 20th century. By the mid-20th century, researchers could identify many diseases caused by a lack of vitamins. So, many nutrient studies were done to prevent vitamin deficiency. At the same time, studies helped to establish a recommended dietary intake and strengthen staple foods.

[3] During the 1950s and 1960s, thanks to economic development, lack of food and vitamins was less of a problem. So, studies on fat and sugar became more common. Especially, fat was thought to be one of the major causes of heart disease, so a low-calorie low-fat diet was strongly recommended.

[4] Between 1970 and 1990, chronic diseases such as obesity, diabetes, and cancer were a big worry. People were advised to avoid too much fat, saturated fat, cholesterol, sugar, and sodium.

[5] From 1990 onwards, studies show that food affects our health in different, complex ways. So, instead of single nutrient research, we need to think about many different factors: quality of fats, types of protein and carbohydrates, micronutrients, processing methods, types of additives used, and so on.

[6] As our understanding grows, we will surely keep changing our eating habits. The important point is to keep a healthy balance and consume the energy and nutrients essential for our growth and health.

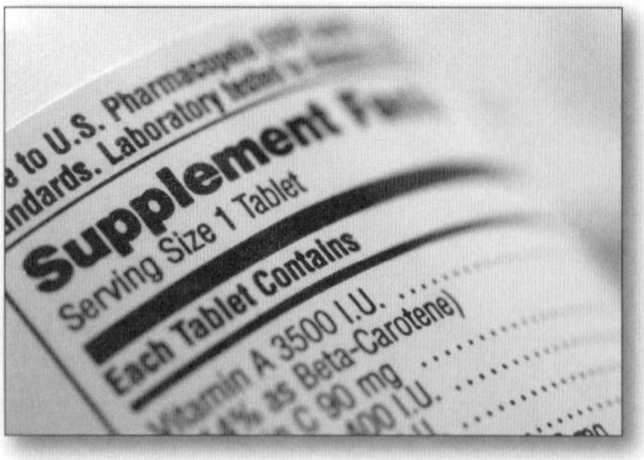


(305 words)

Speed Reading 1st time ( /wpm)
Speed Reading 2nd time ( /wpm)

**NOTES**

**Note: scurvy** 壊血病 **micronutrient** 微量栄養素

## C Scan the Text

**1-5 の日本語の語句と同じ意味の英語の表現を a-e から選び、(　　　　) に記入しましょう。また、本文をよく読み、それらの表現に下線を引きましょう。**

1. 食事摂取　(　　　　　　　　　　)
2. 経済発展　(　　　　　　　　　　)
3. 主食　(　　　　　　　　　　)
4. ビタミンの不足　(　　　　　　　　　　)
5. 慢性疾患　(　　　　　　　　　　)

a. a lack of vitamins
b. staple food
c. dietary intake
d. chronic disease
e. economic development

## D Reading Comprehension

**本文をよく読んで、正しければ T、間違っていれば F に○をつけましょう。**

1. From 1990 onwards, the majority of nutrition research tends to focus on one single factor. **(T / F)**
2. Even though our understanding about nutrition science grows, our eating habits will never change. **(T / F)**

## E Read and Think

**第 2、3、パラグラフから栄養学の進歩をまとめてみましょう。**

20 世紀半ばまでに（①　　　　　）不足を防ぐための栄養の研究が多くなされた。また、同時に推奨される食事摂取と主食の強化が確立された。

1950 年代～1960 年代は（②　　　　　）と（①　　　　　）の不足の問題は減少した。そこで、（③　　　　　）と（④　　　　　）に関する研究がより一般的になった。とりわけ、（③　　　　　）は心臓病の主要な原因の一つと考えられるため、低カロリー低脂肪の食事が強く推奨された。

## F Useful Expressions（instead of）

**下線部に注意して、和訳しましょう。**

1. Instead of single nutrient research, we need to think about many different factors.

----------------------------------------

2. For breakfast, I am going to try eating rice every day instead of bread.

----------------------------------------

## G Over to You

**あなたはバランスのとれた食事をしていると思いますか？　５段階評価で評価し、○をつけてみましょう。**

**１＝全くできていない　２＝あまりできていない　３＝普通　４＝まあまあ、できている　５＝よくできている**

その理由は何ですか？

----------------------------------------

----------------------------------------

----------------------------------------

----------------------------------------

----------------------------------------

### Tea Break

**英語で言えますか？**

症状について英語で言えますか？　病名や症状を下記の選択肢から選びなさい。

① a very strong headache, often accompanied by vision problems and a feeling of sickness: (　　　　　　)

② a rise of body temperature above the normal: (　　　　　　)

③ a skin disorder accompanied by an uncomfortable tickling sensation: (　　　　　　)

④ breathing during sleep with a rough, hoarse noise due to vibration of the soft palate: (　　　　　　)

| snoring | fever | migraine | itch |
|---|---|---|---|

UNIT 3

主食

# Staple Foods

## 考えてみましょう

あなたは朝ごはんにパンを食べますか、それともごはんを食べますか？
また、特別な理由はありますか？

〈メモ〉

What's your staple?

## A Vocabulary Check 8

**次の日本語の意味を表す英語を下の語群から選び、(　　　) 内に書き出しなさい。また、音声を聴いてそれぞれの単語を発音しなさい。**

1. 人口 (　　　　　　　　　　　　　　　　)
2. 食べられる (　　　　　　　　　　　　　　　　)
3. 保存する (　　　　　　　　　　　　　　　　)
4. 地域 (　　　　　　　　　　　　　　　　)
5. 獲得する (　　　　　　　　　　　　　　　　)

語群

store　edible　obtain　population　region

## B Dictation 9

**次の英文を聴き、______ に適切な語句を記入しなさい。**

Most cultures and [1] ____________ have a staple food. People eat that food item [2] ____________ [3] ____________ other foods, and more [4] ____________ : every day, or possibly [5] ____________ times a day.

## Reading Passage 10

[1] What food do you eat more than any other? For many Japanese people, the answer to this question is “rice.” Rice is a good example of a staple food.

[2] Most cultures and societies have a staple food. People eat that food item more than other foods, and more frequently: every day, or possibly many times a day. Typically, staple foods provide plenty of carbohydrates and so they are very important for the survival and health of those who eat them as a staple.

[3] Also, a staple food must be easy to obtain, so it traditionally grows well in the region. It should not be too expensive, because it is the main source of energy and nutrients for most people in the region, and they must be able to afford it. Finally, it should be simple to store and not go bad easily, because it will be the main food source in seasons when not much can grow, such as cold winters or dry summers.

[4] There are many different staple foods. As written above, rice is one example. Other examples include corn (also called maize), wheat, potatoes, yams, and beans. According to the Food and Agriculture Organization of the United Nations, there are 50,000 edible plants around the world, but just three of them (corn, rice, and wheat) provide energy to 60% of the world’s population.

[5] We eat staple foods so much that perhaps we take them for granted. Now you see how important staple foods are to us and to our societies.

(252 words)

| | | | |
|---|---|---|---|
| Speed Reading | 1st time | ( | /wpm) |
| Speed Reading | 2nd time | ( | /wpm) |

## C Scan the Text

**1-5 の日本語の語句と同じ意味の英語の表現を a-e から選び、(　　　　) に記入しましょう。また、本文をよく読み、それらの表現に下線を引きましょう。**

1. 上述のように　(　　　　　　　　　　)
2. 国際連合　(　　　　　　　　　　)
3. それらを当然だと思う　(　　　　　　　　　　)
4. 主要なエネルギー源　(　　　　　　　　　　)
5. （食べ物などが）悪くなる　(　　　　　　　　　　)

a. go bad
b. main source of energy
c. take them for granted
d. the United Nations
e. as written above

## D Reading Comprehension

**本文をよく読んで、正しければ T、間違っていれば F に○をつけましょう。**

1. Staple foods provide us with at least one of the energy-providing nutrients.　(T / F)
2. Beans are an example of a staple food.　(T / F)

## E Read and Think

**第 3 パラグラフを読み、伝統的にその土地の主食となってきた理由をまとめえてみましょう。**

理由①　伝統的にその土地でよく繁茂している。
理由②　入手しやすくないといけないため、高すぎない。
理由③　----------------------------------------

## F *Useful Expressions*（according to）

**下線部に注意して、和訳しましょう。**

1. According to the United Nations, there are 50,000 edible plants around the world.

2. It's important to start the day with a good breakfast, according to my mom.

## G *Over to You*

**和食が外国の食事と異なる点を列挙してみましょう。そして、ペアで比べてみましょう。**

### Tea Break

「食」関連の語彙クイズ

①食品でないのはどれ？（　　　　　　　）

ladle　　vinegar　　tuna　　flour　　horseradish

②魚介類でないのはどれ？（　　　　　　　）

cod　　bonito　　clam　　cucumber　　mackerel

③野菜でないのはどれ？（　　　　　　　）

leek　　detergent　　taro　　celery　　ginger

食の文化遺産

# UNIT 4 The Cultural Heritage of Food

## 考えてみましょう

日本の和食がなぜ、食の文化遺産に選ばれたのか、考えてみましょう。

〈メモ〉

Part of your cultural heritage

## A *Vocabulary Check* 11

**次の日本語の意味を表す英語を下の語群から選び、(　　　) 内に書き出しなさい。また、音声を聴いてそれぞれの単語を発音しなさい。**

1. 宗教的な　(　　　　　　　　　　　　　　　)
2. 評価する　(　　　　　　　　　　　　　　　)
3. 革新的な　(　　　　　　　　　　　　　　　)
4. 支持、賛成　(　　　　　　　　　　　　　　　)
5. 先祖　(　　　　　　　　　　　　　　　)

語群

religious　innovative　ancestor　favor　evaluate

## B *Dictation* 12

**次の英文を聴き、______ に適切な語句を記入しなさい。**

*Washoku* is not the only cuisine included as an intangible cultural heritage. As of [1] ____________, “Traditional [2] ____________ Cuisine,” “The Mediterranean Diet” [3] ____________, Italy, Morocco, [4] ____________, “Croatian Gingerbread Making,” “Turkish Coffee,” and “The Gastronomic Meal of the [5] ____________” are also on the UNESCO list.

# Reading Passage 13

[1] According to UNESCO, "cultural heritage" is not just about monuments and objects; it also refers to "traditions or living expressions inherited from our ancestors and passed on to our descendants" (UNESCO website). This is known as 'Intangible Cultural Heritage.'

[2] In 2013, traditional Japanese cuisine, *washoku*, was designated as a UNESCO Intangible Cultural Heritage. It was appraised for its respect for fresh ingredients, for having healthy and balanced nutrition, for displaying the natural beauty of different seasons, and for having a deep connection with religious and commercial events, and traditional culture.

[3] *Washoku* is not the only cuisine included as an intangible cultural heritage. As of 2018, "Traditional Mexican Cuisine," "The Mediterranean Diet" (Greece, Italy, Morocco, Spain), "Croatian Gingerbread Making," "Turkish Coffee," and "The Gastronomic Meal of the French" are also on the UNESCO list.

[4] Many people are very happy and proud that their cuisine is recognized in this way. The Intangible Cultural Heritage list is designed to raise awareness of culture, and it is good that more people can know about this important part of the culture of a country (or region). The list is also meant to protect culture, and many people believe it is important to protect national cuisine from the globalization of the food industry.

[5] However, some people are not completely in favor. They say that putting cuisine on the Intangible Cultural Heritage list might stop chefs being innovative in their cooking. Also, why are some types of cuisine included on the list but not others? Surely there are many other kinds of cuisine that reflect their unique culture.

[6] What is important is that the list does not 'evaluate' or 'score.' By showing respect to all food cultures and promoting awareness and protection of specific cuisine, the list is certainly a benefit for global food culture.

(298 words)

| | | |
|---|---|---|
| Speed Reading | 1st time ( | /wpm) |
| Speed Reading | 2nd time ( | /wpm) |

## C Scan the Text

**1-5 の日本語の語句と同じ意味の英語の表現を a-e から選び、(　　　　) に記入しましょう。また、本文をよく読み、それらの表現に下線を引きましょう。**

1. 国民的な料理　(　　　　　　　　　　　　　　)
2. 世界的な食文化　(　　　　　　　　　　　　　　)
3. 私たちの子孫へ引き継ぐ　(　　　　　　　　　　　　　　)
4. 食産業　(　　　　　　　　　　　　　　)
5. 文化への理解　(　　　　　　　　　　　　　　)

a. global food culture
b. awareness of culture
c. food industry
d. national cuisine
e. pass on to our descendants

## D Reading Comprehension

**本文をよく読んで、正しければ T、間違っていれば F に○をつけましょう。**

1. *Washoku* was the only cuisine chosen as an intangible cultural heritage. (T / F)
2. The UNESCO list is important because it rates different cuisines. (T / F)

## E Read and Think

**第 5 パラグラフを読み、理由をまとめてみましょう。**

文化遺産への選出について、必ずしも賛成しない（not completely in favor）人々もいる。

理由①------------------------------------------------------------

理由②------------------------------------------------------------

## F *Useful Expressions*（be meant to）

**下線部に注意して、和訳しましょう。**

1. The Intangible Cultural Heritage list <u>is meant to</u> protect culture.

------------------------------------------------------------

2. The labels on food cans <u>are meant to</u> provide information to consumers.

------------------------------------------------------------

## G *Over to You*

**世界各国の料理であなたが好きなのはどこの国の料理ですか。ペアやグループで比べてみましょう。**

------------------------------------------------------------

------------------------------------------------------------

------------------------------------------------------------

------------------------------------------------------------

------------------------------------------------------------

### Tea Break

**各国料理**

その国の特色ある料理を選択肢から選びましょう。

| | Country | Dish |
|---|---|---|
| ex. | Japan | Sushi |
| ① | Spain | |
| ② | Italy | |
| ③ | China | |
| ④ | India | |

Dim Sum　　Risotto　　Tandoori Chicken　　Paella

弁当箱のアート

# UNIT 5 The Art of the Bento Box

## 考えてみましょう

一番、好きなお弁当の具材は何ですか？　ペアで話し合ってみましょう。

〈メモ〉

Nutritious and artistic Japanese *Bento* Box

## A Vocabulary Check 14

**次の日本語の意味を表す英語を下の語群から選び、(　　　)内に書き出しなさい。また、音声を聴いてそれぞれの単語を発音しなさい。**

1. 魅力的な　(　　　　　　　　　　　　)
2. 副菜　(　　　　　　　　　　　　)
3. 価値がある　(　　　　　　　　　　　　)
4. 海藻　(　　　　　　　　　　　　)
5. 目立つ　(　　　　　　　　　　　　)

語群

seaweed　attractive　striking　value　side dishes

## B Dictation 15

**次の英文を聴き、＿＿＿＿に適切な語句を記入しなさい。**

If you google the word “*bento*” in English, you can find many [1] ____________ introducing this Japanese food [2] ____________, details of how to [3] ____________ a *bento*, and pictures of [4] ____________ and carefully-packed *bento* [5] ____________ .

## Reading Passage 16

[1] If you google the word "*bento*" in English, you can find many websites introducing this Japanese food culture, details of how to prepare a *bento*, and pictures of cute and carefully-packed *bento* boxes. It seems that "*bento*" is now a well-known and popular concept around the world.

[2] Now, you sometimes hear the word "*bento*," and sometimes "packed lunch," but what's the difference between them? When you hear the word "packed lunch," you may simply imagine your lunch, whatever it may be, packed into a simple plastic container or even in a plastic bag. "*Bento*," on the other hand, gives the image of a colorfully decorated lunch box containing many ingredients.

[3] Perhaps the most iconic image of this is the "*kyara-ben*"; a name that combines "character" and "*bento*." "*Kyara-ben*" usually contains cute characters shaped as food, such as animals or flower-shaped ingredients, and rice balls with a smiley face made from *nori* seaweed. These boxes are not only visually striking but they are also often made with attention to the balance of nutrients.

[4] Traditional "*makunouchi bento*" is said to be one of the most balanced boxed lunches because it includes a main meat or fish, many side vegetable dishes, and also rice—all while keeping its attractive look.

[5] So why are *bento* boxes getting so much international attention these days? Many believe the beautifully presented box is very symbolic of Japan and Japanese *washoku*, which values not only the health but also the beauty of food. As seen in the Japanese expression "eat food with your eyes," the appearance of the meal matters just as much as the taste!

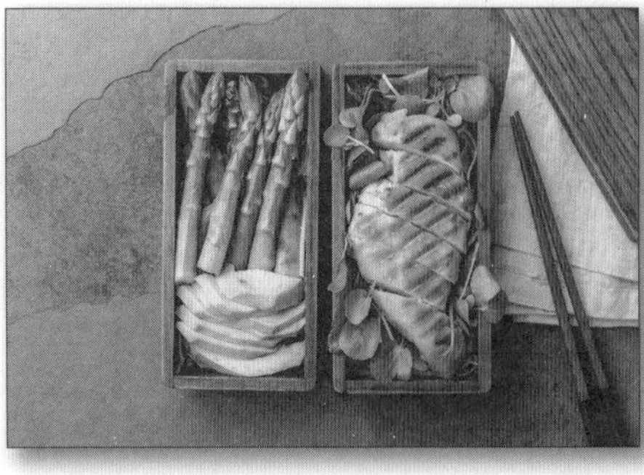

(268 words)

| | | | |
|---|---|---|---|
| Speed Reading | 1st time | ( | /wpm) |
| Speed Reading | 2nd time | ( | /wpm) |

## C Scan the Text

**1-5の日本語の語句と同じ意味の英語の表現をa-eから選び、(　　　　)に記入しましょう。また、本文をよく読み、それらの表現に下線を引きましょう。**

1. おにぎり　(　　　　)
2. プラスチックの容器　(　　　　)
3. 料理は見た目が大事　(　　　　)
4. 象徴的イメージ　(　　　　)
5. ニコちゃんマーク、ニコニコマーク　(　　　　)

a. plastic container
b. eat food with your eyes
c. smiley face
d. iconic image
e. rice ball

## D Reading Comprehension

**本文をよく読んで、正しければT、間違っていればFに○をつけましょう。**

1. *Bento* boxes have attracted international attention. (T / F)
2. *Kyara-ben* is unpopular among teachers as it does not promote healthy eating. (T / F)

## E Read and Think

**第5パラグラフを読み、なぜ、弁当が最近注目されているのか考え、空欄を埋めましょう。**

美しく盛り付けられた弁当は（①　　　　）だけでなく食べ物の（②　　　　）に価値を置く、日本や和食を象徴していると多くの人は考えている。

## F *Useful Expressions*（not only A but also B）

**下線部に注意して、和訳しましょう。**

1. These *bento* boxes are not only visually striking but they are also often made with attention to the balance of nutrients.

----------------------------------------

2. I love not only the flavor but also the texture of avocados.

----------------------------------------

## G *Over to You*

**「日本」をイメージしたキャラ弁をデザインしてみましょう。できたら、ペアで比較してみましょう。**

### Tea Break

**食と関連する動詞の活用**

空欄（過去形、過去分詞）を埋めましょう。

| 原形 | 過去形 | 過去分詞 |
| --- | --- | --- |
| eat | | |
| drink | | |
| feed | | |
| cut | | |
| knead | | |

日本の給食制度

# UNIT 6 Kyushoku: The Japanese School Lunch

## 考えてみましょう

小学生の頃を思い出してください。好きな給食のメニューは何でしたか？

〈メモ〉

A healthy and educational school lunch

## A Vocabulary Check 17

**次の日本語の意味を表す英語を下の語群から選び、(　　　) 内に書き出しなさい。また、音声を聴いてそれぞれの単語を発音しなさい。**

1. 機会 (　　　　　　　　　　　　　　)
2. 鉄分 (　　　　　　　　　　　　　　)
3. 教育 (　　　　　　　　　　　　　　)
4. 雑用、家事 (　　　　　　　　　　　　　　)
5. 栄養士 (　　　　　　　　　　　　　　)

語群

nutritionist　　education　　opportunity　　chore　　iron

## B Dictation 18

**次の英文を聴き、______ に適切な語句を記入しなさい。**

The *kyushoku* school lunch is provided in most [1] __________ and junior high schools throughout Japan. There are three main differences between *kyushoku* and school lunches provided in [2] __________ countries: 1) students eat in the classroom instead of the [3] __________ ; 2) [4] __________ take part in the serving; 3) usually only one set menu is [5] __________ each day.

## Reading Passage 19

[1] The *kyushoku* school lunch is provided in most elementary and junior high schools throughout Japan. There are three main differences between *kyushoku* and school lunches provided in other countries: 1) students eat in the classroom instead of the cafeteria; 2) children take part in the serving; 3) usually only one set menu is offered each day.

[2] Because there is a set menu, nutritionists can make sure students get the necessary nutrients every day. In fact, the Japanese government has a detailed policy on *kyushoku*; for example, meals must contain ⅓ of the daily recommended amount of most key nutritional elements. One-third to half of vitamins and minerals that are said to be lacking from children's diets, such as iron and vitamins A, B1, and B2, can also be included.

[3] Offering a balanced diet is not the only positive element of *kyushoku*. It also provides education in healthy eating, improved social skills, and understanding of the importance of chores. In fact, the program has been widely praised around the world. Some specialists believe *kyushoku* is partly the reason for lower rates of obesity among Japanese children compared to children in countries such as the U.S.

[4] Compared to the western-style school lunch, *kyushoku* doesn't seem to be too exciting for Japanese school kids: they have no choice about the menu, and there are no vending machines to pick snacks from. However, by learning more about a variety of food and tasting many different dishes, students gain many opportunities to understand healthy eating from a young age.

(254 words)

| | | | |
|---|---|---|---|
| Speed Reading | 1st time | ( | /wpm) |
| Speed Reading | 2nd time | ( | /wpm) |

## C *Scan the Text*

**1-5 の日本語の語句と同じ意味の英語の表現を a-e から選び、(　　　　) に記入しましょう。また、本文をよく読み、それらの表現に下線を引きましょう。**

1. ～のような　(　　　　　　　　)
2. 選択肢がない　(　　　　　　　　)
3. 社交術 , 社会適応能力　(　　　　　　　　)
4. 賞賛する　(　　　　　　　　)
5. 自動販売機　(　　　　　　　　)

a. praise
b. such as
c. no choice
d. vending machine
e. social skills

## D *Reading Comprehension*

**本文をよく読んで、正しければ T、間違っていれば F に○をつけましょう。**

1. Japanese school lunch programs are seen in a positive way around the world. **(T / F)**
2. *Kyushoku* seems exciting compared to western-style school lunches. **(T / F)**

## E *Read and Think*

**第 2 パラグラフを読み、日本の給食の特徴をまとめてみましょう。**

決まった献立のため、児童は毎日、必要な（①　　　　　）を摂取できることを栄養士が確認できる。（②　　　　　）は給食に対して詳細な方針があり、給食は主要な栄養素の一日の推奨量の（③　　　　　）を含まなければならない。

## F *Useful Expressions*（in fact）

**下線部に注意して、和訳しましょう。**

1. In fact, the Japanese government has a strict policy on *kyushoku*.

2. I love sushi. In fact, I like all Japanese food.

## G *Over to You*

**選べるとしたら、給食と弁当、どちらが好きですか？　その理由は何ですか？**

### Tea Break

**知っていますか？**

クイズ：体重 50kg の人がシュークリーム 1 個と同じエネルギーを消費するためには、ヨガであればどのくらい行えばよいでしょうか？

シュークリーム 1 個（90g：210kcal）

A　約 30 分
B　約 100 分
C　約 240 分

UNIT 7

# こども食堂

# *Kodomo Shokudo*

## 考えてみましょう

子供の人権について、どんなものがあるでしょうか？　考えてみましょう。

〈メモ〉

A place to eat and socialize

## A *Vocabulary Check* 20

**次の日本語の意味を表す英語を下の語群から選び、(　　　) 内に書き出しなさい。また、音声を聴いてそれぞれの単語を発音しなさい。**

1. ごみ　(　　　　　　　　　　　　)
2. 交流する　(　　　　　　　　　　　　)
3. 価値ある　(　　　　　　　　　　　　)
4. 貧困　(　　　　　　　　　　　　)
5. その間　(　　　　　　　　　　　　)

**語群**

socialize　poverty　meantime　valuable　waste

## B *Dictation* 21

**次の英文を聴き、______ に適切な語句を記入しなさい。**

According to the World Health Organization (WHO), hundreds of millions of [1] ____________ under [2] ____________ years old are undernourished. This means that a [3] ____________ of adequate nutrition harms their physical and [4] ____________ development, and it could also lead to [5] ____________.

## Reading Passage 22

[1] Access to food and nutrition is a basic human right. However, according to the World Health Organization (WHO), hundreds of millions of children under five years old are undernourished. This means that a lack of adequate nutrition harms their physical and mental development, and it could also lead to death.

[2] The problem of undernutrition is not only in developing countries. According to a 2012 survey in Japan, about 16% of two-parent families have difficulties providing enough food for their children, and the rate doubles for single-parent families.

[3] However, one program is making a difference. Kodomo Shokudo (which translates as "kids' cafeteria") has been established in many locations in Japan, and it aims to provide a meal for children, and a place to socialize and spend time with others.

[4] Specialists believe that the Kodomo Shokudo program has various benefits. Children who come to Kodomo Shokudo report that they can eat healthier food than at home, and they also enjoy dining with others like in a big family. It allows parents to socialize with each other, and allows grandparents to volunteer and stay connected with the community. What's more, the food there is often donated by local businesses that would otherwise throw it away, so the program helps to avoid unnecessary waste.

[5] Of course, the causes of poverty and undernutrition in Japan must be researched and understood more deeply. In the meantime, Kodomo Shokudo is providing a very valuable service for families throughout the country.

(243 words)

| | | | |
|---|---|---|---|
| Speed Reading | 1st time | ( | /wpm) |
| Speed Reading | 2nd time | ( | /wpm) |

## C Scan the Text

**1-5 の日本語の語句と同じ意味の英語の表現を a-e から選び、(　　　　　) に記入しましょう。また、本文をよく読み、それらの表現に下線を引きましょう。**

1. 開発途上国　　　　(　　　　　　　　　　　　　　)
2. 全国で　　　　　　(　　　　　　　　　　　　　　)
3. 様々な効果　　　　(　　　　　　　　　　　　　　)
4. (それを) 捨てる　(　　　　　　　　　　　　　　)
5. 状況を良くする、改善する　(　　　　　　　　　　　　　　)

a. making a difference
b. various benefits
c. throughout the country
d. throw it away
e. developing countries

## D Reading Comprehension

**本文をよく読んで、正しければ T、間違っていれば F に○をつけましょう。**

1. In Japan, the problem of undernutrition has been solved.　(T / F)
2. Local companies support Kodomo Shokudo financially.　(T / F)

## E Read and Think

**第 4 パラグラフを読み、専門家の考える「こども食堂の子供にとっての利点」をまとめてみましょう。**

子供たちは家庭よりも（①　　　　　　）的な食べ物を食べることができ、（②　　　　　　）のように他の人たちと食事を楽しめる。

## F Useful Expressions（what's more）

**下線部に注意して、和訳しましょう。**

1. Kodomo Shokudo allows parents to socialize with each other. What's more, the food is often donated by local businesses.

2. I've had more energy since I started eating healthily. What's more, I think my skin looks better.

## G Over to You

**食に関するボランティア活動はどんなことがあるか、まとめてみましょう。**

### Tea Break

**調理方法に関する表現**

日本語に合うように、選択肢から選んで（　）を埋めましょう。

① 米を研ぐ　（　　　　　　　）rice

② 塩をふる　（　　　　　　　）salt

③ 生地をこねる　（　　　　　　　）dough

④ 火加減を調節する　（　　　　　　　）the heat

⑤ 小麦粉をふるう　（　　　　　　　）flour

| | | | | |
|---|---|---|---|---|
| adjust | sprinkle | wash | sift | knead |

# UNIT 8

スーパーフード

# Can Foods Be Super?

## 考えてみましょう

雑誌やテレビでスーパーフードが宣伝されていますが、あなたは食べたことがありますか？　ペアで話し合ってみましょう。

〈メモ〉

Superfood or marketing technique?

## A Vocabulary Check 23

次の日本語の意味を表す英語を下の語群から選び、(　　　) 内に書き出しなさい。また、音声を聴いてそれぞれの単語を発音しなさい。

1. ほうれん草　(　　　　　　　　　　)
2. サケ　(　　　　　　　　　　)
3. 誤解されやすい　(　　　　　　　　　　)
4. レッテルを貼る　(　　　　　　　　　　)
5. 栄養補助食品・サプリメント　(　　　　　　　　　　)

語群

spinach　label　misleading　supplement　salmon

## B Dictation 24

次の英文を聴き、_______ に適切な語句を記入しなさい。

In [1] ____________ years, the word “superfood” has been [2] ____________ more and more. In [3] ____________ blogs, [4] ____________, TV reports, supermarkets, and so on, you now see that word very often. So, what [5] ____________ is a superfood?

# Reading Passage 25

[1] In recent years, the word "superfood" has been used more and more. In online blogs, newspapers, TV reports, supermarkets, and so on, you now see that word very often. So, what exactly is a superfood?

[2] Actually, the word itself is just a marketing technique. Companies found that by labeling a food as a "superfood," health- and diet-conscious people became more interested in that food. So, the company could not only sell more of the food but also sell related supplements, diet books, and so on. They said that a superfood could have very positive health effects and could help prevent serious illnesses like heart disease and cancer. Therefore, many different foods, such as blueberries, spinach, and salmon were called "superfoods," and sales went up.

[3] Indeed, many dieticians and nutritionists have pointed out that the word "superfood" is misleading. In fact, in 2007, the European Union banned companies from using the word "superfood," unless they could give scientific evidence of direct health benefits.

[4] Some foods are certainly very good for you—maybe better than others. The Harvard Medical School Health Blog says that eating berries, fish, leafy greens, nuts, olive oil, and other specific foods can be good for your health and help fight diseases. But, the blog also makes the point that there is not one single "superfood" that can provide all of our nutrition and energy while also providing health benefits. As is always the case with diet, the best way is to have a balanced combination of all these different foods, and not to overeat.

[5] So, can foods be super? Yes. Can one food by itself be a superfood? No!

(272 words)

| | | | |
|---|---|---|---|
| Speed Reading | 1st time | ( | /wpm) |
| Speed Reading | 2nd time | ( | /wpm) |

## C Scan the Text

**1-5 の日本語の語句と同じ意味の英語の表現を a-e から選び、(　　　　)に記入しましょう。また、本文をよく読み、それらの表現に下線を引きましょう。**

1. 科学的証拠　(　　　　　　　　)
2. 食べ過ぎない　(　　　　　　　　)
3. 健康や食事に関心がある人々　(　　　　　　　　)
4. 特定の食品　(　　　　　　　　)
5. 葉物野菜　(　　　　　　　　)

a. scientific evidence
b. not to overeat
c. health- and diet-conscious people
d. leafy green
e. specific foods

## D Reading Comprehension

**本文をよく読んで、正しければ T、間違っていれば F に○をつけましょう。**

1. Companies tried to sell foods as well as related supplements and books by using the label "superfood."　**(T / F)**
2. In EU countries, companies cannot call a product a "superfood" without showing scientific evidence of direct health benefits.　**(T / F)**

## E Read and Think

**第 4 パラグラフを読み、Harvard Medical School Health Blog の主張を要約してみましょう。**

(①　　　　　)(②　　　　　)(③　　　　　)(④　　　　　)(⑤　　　　　)やその他の特定の食品は健康や闘病には良いといえる。しかし、健康上の利益を与えつつ、すべての栄養素やエネルギーを与えることのできるたった一つの(⑥　　　　　)はない。

## F *Useful Expressions*（more and more）

**下線部に注意して、和訳しましょう。**

1. In recent years, the word "superfood" has been used more and more.

2. More and more people are becoming interested in nutrition and healthy eating.

## G *Over to You*

**あなたは体に良いと思って心がけて食べている食品はありますか？　どのくらいの頻度で食べていますか？　どのような調理方法をしていますか？　ペアで話してみましょう。**

### Tea Break

**知っておきたい国際機関**

① 国際連合児童基金　(　　　　　　　　)
② 国際連合教育科学文化機関　(　　　　　　　　)
③ 国際連合食糧農業機関　(　　　　　　　　)
④ 世界貿易機関　(　　　　　　　　)
⑤ 世界保健機関　(　　　　　　　　)
⑥ 欧州連合　(　　　　　　　　)

| | | | | | |
|---|---|---|---|---|---|
| WTO | FAO | UNESCO | UNICEF | EU | WHO |

UNIT 9

# ハラルフード

# Halal Food

## 考えてみましょう

あなたは宗教による食の制限について、知っていますか？　知っている人はどんなものがあるか書き出してみましょう。

〈メモ〉

Halal awareness on the rise

## A Vocabulary Check 26

次の日本語の意味を表す英語を下の語群から選び、(　　　) 内に書き出しなさい。また、音声を聴いてそれぞれの単語を発音しなさい。

1. 制限 (　　　　　　　　　　　　)
2. 経歴、生い立ち (　　　　　　　　　　　　)
3. アルコール (　　　　　　　　　　　　)
4. イスラム教徒 (　　　　　　　　　　　　)
5. 禁じる (　　　　　　　　　　　　)

語群

Muslims　　background　　alcohol　　prohibit　　restriction

## B Dictation 27

次の英文を聴き、______ に適切な語句を記入しなさい。

As more people from around the [1] ____________ visit Japan, many places such as hotels and [2] ____________ are doing their best to [3] ____________ all customers' needs. However, providing suitable food is not [4] ____________ easy. Some choose not to eat certain foods for ethical, environmental, and [5] ____________ reasons.

# Reading Passage 28

[1] As more people from around the world visit Japan, many places such as hotels and restaurants are doing their best to meet all customers' needs. However, providing suitable food is not always easy. Some choose not to eat certain foods for ethical, environmental, and health reasons. For example, there are vegetarians who do not eat meat, people who only eat food grown or produced locally, and so on.

[2] However, there are also many people who do not eat certain ingredients due to their culture or religion. One widely known religious food tradition is "halal" food. Muslims cannot have certain food or ingredients, such as alcohol or pork, because these ingredients are not "halal." If another ingredient touches prohibited items during food preparation, Muslims are not to have these dishes.

[3] The rules are actually very complex, and the interpretation of these rules is different according to different groups within the religion. This might make it hard for non-Muslims to fully understand. However, this does not mean we should be completely ignorant about the culture of Muslim people. Organizations such as the Japan Halal Foundation and Japan Halal Business Association provide useful information about halal food and promote awareness by giving workshops and seminars. They also help Muslim travelers find suitable travel services including tours and accommodation.

[4] For many people, trying different foods is one of the attractions of travel. For some people, though, a totally new food culture can be stressful. As an international country that welcomes many tourists from overseas, Japan should learn more about different food cultures —including some cultures' food restrictions—so that it can welcome travelers from any background with the celebrated Japanese hospitality.

(277 words)

| | | | |
|---|---|---|---|
| Speed Reading | 1st time | ( | /wpm) |
| Speed Reading | 2nd time | ( | /wpm) |

## C Scan the Text

**1-5 の日本語の語句と同じ意味の英語の表現を a-e から選び、(　　　　　) に記入しましょう。また、本文をよく読み、それらの表現に下線を引きましょう。**

1. 彼らの文化や宗教のために　(　　　　　　　　　　)
2. 食べ物の調理　(　　　　　　　　　　)
3. これらのルールの解釈　(　　　　　　　　　　)
4. 役に立つ情報を提供する　(　　　　　　　　　　)
5. ツアーや宿泊施設　(　　　　　　　　　　)

a. food preparation
b. the interpretation of these rules
c. tours and accommodation
d. due to their culture or religion
e. provide useful information

## D Reading Comprehension

**本文をよく読んで、正しければ T、間違っていれば F に○をつけましょう。**

1. The rules regarding halal food are very simple.　**(T / F)**
2. Some organizations in Japan give workshops and seminars about halal food.　**(T / F)**

## E Read and Think

**第 2 パラグラフを読み、(　) 内を埋めてみましょう。**

イスラム教徒は（①　　　　　　）や（②　　　　　　）肉を使った食材は「ハラルではない」として食べることができず、「ハラルではない」食品に触れた食材も食べることができない。

## F *Useful Expressions*（actually）

**下線部に注意して、和訳しましょう。**

1. The rules of Halal are actually very complex.

------------------------------------------------------------

2. I used to think cooking for myself would be hard, but actually it’s very easy.

------------------------------------------------------------

## G *Over to You*

**海外からのお客様をもてなすメニューをグループで考えてみましょう。**

### Tea Break

**知っていますか？**

野菜や果物に多く含まれるビタミンCは、皮膚や細胞のコラーゲン合成に必須で、また心臓病の予防効果などが期待されています。積極的に摂取しましょう。

1日の摂取目標量：野菜（350g）、果物（100～200g程度）

参考：日本食品成分表2019七訂：医歯薬出版、健康日本21（第二次）：厚生労働省、農林水産省

クイズ：Vitamin Cが最も多い食べ物はどれでしょうか？

A　いちご（6個：100g）

B　ブロッコリー（4房：100g）

C　みかん（1個：100g）

味が肝心

# How We Taste

## 考えてみましょう

風邪をひいて鼻がつまっているとき、食べ物の風味が違うと思ったことはありませんか？　ペアで話し合ってみましょう。

〈メモ〉

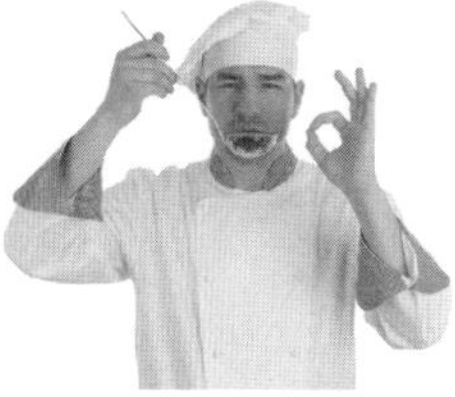

It's all a matter of taste!

## A Vocabulary Check 29

次の日本語の意味を表す英語を下の語群から選び、(　　　) 内に書き出しなさい。また、音声を聴いてそれぞれの単語を発音しなさい。

1. 食べられない　(　　　　　　　　　　　　　　)
2. 飲み込む　(　　　　　　　　　　　　　　)
3. のど　(　　　　　　　　　　　　　　)
4. 詰まる　(　　　　　　　　　　　　　　)
5. はき出す　(　　　　　　　　　　　　　　)

語群

spit　throat　block　swallow　inedible

## B Dictation 30

次の英文を聴き、______ に適切な語句を記入しなさい。

It is [1] __________ said that different parts of the tongue are more [2] __________ for the different tastes of sweet, [3] __________, salty, [4] __________, and savory (for example, "the [5] __________ left of the tongue is where we taste saltiness").

# Reading Passage 31

[1] Have you ever noticed that food tastes different when you have a cold? That's because your sense of taste actually comes from a combination of taste buds in the mouth and sensory signals in the nose. People have between 5,000 and 10,000 taste buds in the mouth, and these are what give you the sense of sweet, sour, salty, bitter, or savory (also known as *umami*—from the Japanese うまい —as it was first identified by Japanese professor Kikunae Ikeda in 1908).

[2] The sensory signals in the nose add more 'detail' to our sense, and the combination of the basic sensations from the mouth and the detail from the nose are what we think of as 'flavor.' So when your nose is blocked, you are only getting the taste, and not the flavor!

[3] It is sometimes said that different parts of the tongue are more sensitive for the different tastes of sweet, sour, salty, bitter, and savory (for example, "the front left of the tongue is where we taste saltiness"). However, this is not correct; most of the five basic tastes are perceived equally on the tongue, although there are more taste buds around the sides and back and fewer in the middle.

[4] There is, however, one exception; the back of the tongue is more sensitive to detecting bitterness. There is probably an evolutionary reason for this; a bitter flavor may indicate that a food is inedible or even poisonous. So, before the food comes into contact with the throat or is swallowed, the sensors at the back of the tongue can detect the bitterness and force you to spit the food out. In this case, taste certainly does matter!

(279 words)

| | | | |
|---|---|---|---|
| Speed Reading | 1st time | ( | /wpm) |
| Speed Reading | 2nd time | ( | /wpm) |

## C Scan the Text

**1-5 の日本語の語句と同じ意味の英語の表現を a-e から選び、(　　　　) に記入しましょう。また、本文をよく読み、それらの表現に下線を引きましょう。**

1. 味《み》蕾《らい》　(　　　　　　　　　　　　)
2. 舌の奥　(　　　　　　　　　　　　)
3. 苦さを検知する　(　　　　　　　　　　　　)
4. 進化的な理由　(　　　　　　　　　　　　)
5. 真ん中　(　　　　　　　　　　　　)

a. taste buds
b. in the middle
c. evolutionary reason
d. the back of the tongue
e. detect bitterness

## D Reading Comprehension

**本文をよく読んで、正しければ T、間違っていれば F に○をつけましょう。**

1. A Japanese professor identified the sense of bitterness about 100 years ago. **(T / F)**
2. The middle of the tongue is more sensitive than the back. **(T / F)**

## E Read and Think

**第 4 パラグラフをよく読み、食べられないものや毒物を含む食べ物を検知したかもしれないとき、口の中のセンサーはどのように反応するか、簡単にまとめてみましょう。**

食べ物が（①　　　　　）に触れたり、飲み込んだりする前に、（②　　　　　）の奥にあるセンサーが（③　　　　　）を検知して、食べ物を吐き出させる。

## F *Useful Expressions*（have you ever ...?）

**下線部に注意して、和訳しましょう。**

1. Have you ever noticed that food tastes different when you have a cold?

2. Have you ever prepared your own *bento* box for lunch?

## G *Over to You*

**あなたは食品を買うときにどんなことが気になりますか？　気になることには○、まあまあ気になる場合には△、気にならないことには×、をつけましょう。**

(　　　) 値段
(　　　) 賞味期限・消費期限
(　　　) 生産地・生産者
(　　　) 食品添加物の有無や種類
(　　　) その他　具体的に

### Tea Break

**英語で言えますか？**

体の器官を下記の選択肢から選びなさい。

① a joint in the middle of the arm　(　　　　　)
② the part of the face above the eyes　(　　　　　)
③ a joint in the middle of the leg　(　　　　　)
④ a joint at the top of the arm　(　　　　　)

| | | | |
|---|---|---|---|
| knee | forehead | shoulder | elbow |

機内食

UNIT 11

# Airline Food

## 考えてみましょう

飛行機や新幹線で出される機内食や駅弁で、思い出があれば、ペアでシェアしてみましょう。

〈メモ〉

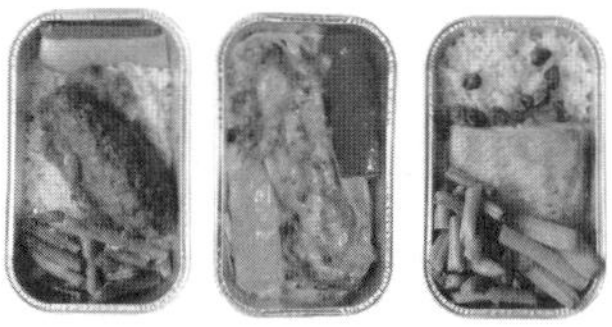

Safe and tasty airline food

## A Vocabulary Check 32

**次の日本語の意味を表す英語を下の語群から選び、(　　　) 内に書き出しなさい。また、音声を聴いてそれぞれの単語を発音しなさい。**

1. 複雑な　(　　　　　　　　　　　　　　　　)
2. 再加熱　(　　　　　　　　　　　　　　　　)
3. 味付けをする　(　　　　　　　　　　　　　　　　)
4. 大気、空気　(　　　　　　　　　　　　　　　　)
5. 湿気　(　　　　　　　　　　　　　　　　)

**語群**

complicated　humidity　reheat　atmosphere　season

## B Dictation 33

**次の英文を聴き、______ に適切な語句を記入しなさい。**

Every year, [1] ____________ of tickets are sold for [2] ____________ all over the world. Many of the [3] ____________ on these flights are given an in-flight [4] ____________. Of course, this meal has to be safe—it would be [5] ____________ for the airline if many passengers got food poisoning.

# Reading Passage 34

[1] Every year, billions of tickets are sold for flights all over the world. Many of the passengers on these flights are given an in-flight meal. Of course, this meal has to be safe—it would be bad for the airline if many passengers got food poisoning. However, what many people do not realize is the amount of research and effort made in order to also make the food taste good.

[2] One big problem is that the meal must be cooked before being taken onto the plane, and then reheated when in the air. This is to prevent food poisoning. Therefore, a lot of research is done about how to stop food becoming dry or tasteless, even though it is first cooked long before it is eaten.

[3] However, there are bigger difficulties in making food taste good up in the air. In a plane at 9,000 meters, the air pressure is low and the air is very dry: humidity is less than 12%. In such a dry atmosphere we do not smell properly, which (as we saw in Unit 10) affects our taste, especially our sense of sweet and salty flavors. So, airlines have to season food much more, adding salt and sugar to make the food taste good 1 km in the sky.

[4] Another issue is our sense of hearing. Research shows that eating with a lot of background noise can make food taste less sweet and less salty. The type of music we listen to also affects our sense of taste. So, some airlines offer meals with noise-canceling headphones and music carefully selected to bring out the flavors of the food.

[5] The science behind airline food is more complicated than most people realize. Next time you fly, if the food tastes good, now you'll know why!

(297 words)

| | | | |
|---|---|---|---|
| Speed Reading | 1st time | ( | /wpm) |
| Speed Reading | 2nd time | ( | /wpm) |

## C Scan the Text

**1-5 の日本語の語句と同じ意味の英語の表現を a-e から選び、(　　　　) に記入しましょう。また、本文をよく読み、それらの表現に下線を引きましょう。**

1. 味気がない　(　　　　　　　　　　　　　　　　)
2. 機内食　　　(　　　　　　　　　　　　　　　　)
3. 味覚　　　　(　　　　　　　　　　　　　　　　)
4. 聴覚　　　　(　　　　　　　　　　　　　　　　)
5. 食中毒　　　(　　　　　　　　　　　　　　　　)

a. in-flight meal
b. food poisoning
c. sense of hearing
d. sense of taste
e. tasteless

## D Reading Comprehension

**本文をよく読んで、正しければ T、間違っていれば F に○をつけましょう。**

1. Our sense of hearing is connected with how we sense sweetness.　(T / F)
2. The science behind in-flight meals is much simpler than you think.　(T / F)

## E Read and Think

**第 2 パラグラフを読み、(　) 内を埋めてみましょう。**

大きな問題は機内食を持ち込む前に調理しなければならないことである。(①　　　　　　) を防ぐために機内に持ち込む前に調理され、機内で再加熱される。そのため、(②　　　　　　) したり、味気なくなったりしないようにする方法について、多くの研究がなされている。

## F Useful Expressions（more ~ than）

**下線部に注意して、和訳しましょう。**

1. The science behind airline food is more complicated than most people realize.

----------------------------------------

2. My brother checks the labels on food packaging more carefully than I do.

----------------------------------------

## G Over to You

**あなたの出身地の特産物を使った機内食を考えてみましょう。できたら、ペアで比較してみましょう。**

### Tea Break

**「食」を楽しむ映画 Culinary Cinema—『マダム・マローリーと魔法のスパイス』**

海外の食文化に興味はあるけれど、なかなか外国に行く機会がないという学生は、食をテーマにした映画 Culinary Cinema で雰囲気を味わってみるのも良いですね。お薦めの一本は、『マダム・マローリーと魔法のスパイス』（The Hundred-foot Journey　2014）。フランス料理店の前に移住してきたインド人一家がレストランを開店したことで起こる摩擦を描いた映画です。インド料理、フランス料理、移民問題、ミシュランガイドなど、この一本で楽しみながら学べます。

UNIT 12

砂糖：知っておくべきこと

# Sugar: What You Need to Know

## 考えてみましょう

あなたは間食に甘い物を摂る習慣がありますか？　ペア、またはグループで話し合ってみましょう。

〈メモ〉

Sugar: how much is too much?

## A Vocabulary Check 35

**次の日本語の意味を表す英語を下の語群から選び、(　　　) 内に書き出しなさい。また、音声を聴いてそれぞれの単語を発音しなさい。**

1. 恐ろしい　(　　　　　　　　　　)
2. 認知症　(　　　　　　　　　　)
3. 鬱《うつ》病　(　　　　　　　　　　)
4. 精製された砂糖　(　　　　　　　　　　)
5. 血糖　(　　　　　　　　　　)

語群

refined sugar　　depression　　frightening　　dementia　　blood sugar

## B Dictation 36

**次の英文を聴き、_______ に適切な語句を記入しなさい。**

Sugar makes food and drink taste [1] ____________, or so many [2] ____________ think. But, many of us take in too much added sugar. The World Health Organization [3] ____________ recommends getting less than [4] ____________ % of our total [5] ____________ intake from sugars.

# Reading Passage 37

[1] As we saw in Unit 1, our main source of energy comes from carbohydrates, and sugar is a simple carbohydrate. Simply, sugars can be divided into two types. The first is natural sugars, which you find in fruits, milk, and dairy products. The second is refined sugars, which are extracted from sugar cane or sugar beets. This is the kind of sugar that is added to many of the foods and drinks you find in the supermarket today.

[2] Sugar makes food and drink taste better, or so many people think. But, many of us take in too much added sugar. The World Health Organization strongly recommends getting less than 10% of our total energy intake from sugars (and less than 5% would be even better). However, in the U.S. in 1999-2000, people's average energy from sugar was 18.1%. In 2013-2014, it was 13.4%. This means we are going in the right direction, but it is still far too high.

[3] Also, what is sugar actually doing to you? The health risks of consuming too much sugar are frightening. Studies show that too much can lead to heart disease, cancer, diabetes, obesity, depression, tooth decay, bad skin, and possibly even dementia. As for the energy it gives us; after a short energy boost, blood sugar drops quickly, and we experience a 'crash,' or sudden loss of energy.

[4] Of course, not all sugars are bad for you, and sugar in moderation (as with most things) is not necessarily bad. However, make sure you know how much sugar you are consuming—that knowledge could keep you healthy!

(263 words)

| | | |
|---|---|---|
| Speed Reading | 1st time | ( /wpm) |
| Speed Reading | 2nd time | ( /wpm) |

## C *Scan the Text*

**1-5 の日本語の語句と同じ意味の英語の表現を a-e から選び、(　　　　　) に記入しましょう。また、本文をよく読み、それらの表現に下線を引きましょう。**

1. 虫歯 (　　　　　　　　　　　　　　)
2. 抽出する (　　　　　　　　　　　　　　)
3. 知識 (　　　　　　　　　　　　　　)
4. 乳製品 (　　　　　　　　　　　　　　)
5. 正しい方向 (　　　　　　　　　　　　　　)

a. dairy products
b. extract
c. tooth decay
d. knowledge
e. right direction

## D *Reading Comprehension*

**本文をよく読んで、正しければ T、間違っていれば F に○をつけましょう。**

1. Consuming too much sugar creates various risks for your body. (T / F)
2. As not all sugars are bad for us, we can consume sugar in moderation. (T / F)

## E *Read and Think*

**第 1 パラグラフを読み、糖質を二つに分けてみましょう。**

一つ目は果物や牛乳、(①　　　　　) に見られる自然の糖分です。二番目は、精製された砂糖で、(②　　　　　) や (③　　　　　) から抽出されるものです。これは、皆さんが今日、スーパーマーケットで見る食べ物や飲み物の多くに添加されている種類の糖質です。

## F *Useful Expressions*（make sure）

**下線部に注意して、和訳しましょう。**

1. Make sure you know how much sugar you are consuming.

2. I always make sure that the food I buy doesn’t contain added sugar.

## G *Over to You*

**あなたは自分が1日にどれだけ砂糖を摂取しているか気をつけていますか？　5段階評価で評価し、○をつけてみましょう。**

**1＝全く気にしていない　2＝あまり気にしていない　3＝普通　4＝まあまあ、気をつけている　5＝気をつけている**

その理由は何ですか？

### Tea Break

**おいしいお菓子**

英語の定義から、何のお菓子を言っているのかわかりますか？　選択肢から選んでみましょう。

① a candy made of chocolate, butter, and sugar　(　　　　　)

② a small usually ring-shaped piece of sweet fried dough　(　　　　　)

③ a cold dessert made of layers of fruit, syrup, ice cream, and whipped cream　(　　　　　)

| | | |
|---|---|---|
| donut | truffle | parfait |

UNIT 13

砂糖税

# Sugar Tax

## 考えてみましょう

甘い飲み物とお茶、どちらが好きですか？　ペアで話し合ってみましょう。

〈メモ〉

Taxing sugar: A good idea?

## A Vocabulary Check 38

**次の日本語の意味を表す英語を下の語群から選び、(　　　)内に書き出しなさい。また、音声を聴いてそれぞれの単語を発音しなさい。**

1. 罰則　(　　　　　　　　　　)
2. 解決策　(　　　　　　　　　　)
3. 導入する　(　　　　　　　　　　)
4. 消費する、食する　(　　　　　　　　　　)
5. 取り組む　(　　　　　　　　　　)

語群

punishment　consume　solution　introduce　tackle

## B Dictation 39

**次の英文を聴き、_______ に適切な語句を記入しなさい。**

Diet-related problems are [1] ___________: 63% of British adults are now [2] ___________ or obese; every [3] ___________ minutes, a [4] ___________ in England has a tooth [5] ___________ because of tooth decay.

## Reading Passage 40

[1] Diet-related problems are increasing: 63% of British adults are now overweight or obese; every 10 minutes, a child in England has a tooth removed because of tooth decay. These numbers are shocking, and one cause is the amount of sugar we consume, especially in sugary drinks, such as cola.

[2] So, in April 2018, the UK started charging a "sugar tax." If a drink contains more than 5g of sugar per 100ml, the drink company has to pay an extra tax of 18p (about ¥26) per liter. If the drink contains more than 8g, the tax goes up to 24p (about ¥35). Thirty other countries have introduced a similar tax in recent years.

[3] The hope is that three things will happen: 1) companies choose to put less sugar in their drinks to avoid the tax. Some companies have already done this, but two of the most famous, Coca-Cola and Pepsi, have not changed their drinks at all; 2) customers choose to buy cheaper, non-taxed drinks that have less sugar; 3) the government can spend the extra tax money to tackle diabetes, obesity, tooth decay, and other problems often caused by bad diet.

[4] However, not everybody supports this sugar tax. Some people say that education is more important than 'punishment' and that consuming sugar is a personal choice. Also, some do not think this tax will work, because people who really want sugary drinks will just pay more.

[5] Most people agree that we need to do something about the high levels of sugar in our diet. The sugar tax may or may not be the solution, but hopefully it will at least make people think more about their sugar intake.

(278 words)

| | | | |
|---|---|---|---|
| Speed Reading | 1st time | ( | /wpm) |
| Speed Reading | 2nd time | ( | /wpm) |

## C Scan the Text

**1-5の日本語の語句と同じ意味の英語の表現をa-eから選び、(　　　　)に記入しましょう。また、本文をよく読み、それらの表現に下線を引きましょう。**

1. 飲料水の会社　(　　　　　　　　　　　　　　　　　)
2. 近年　　　　　(　　　　　　　　　　　　　　　　　)
3. 悪い食習慣　　(　　　　　　　　　　　　　　　　　)
4. 個人の選択　　(　　　　　　　　　　　　　　　　　)
5. 砂糖の摂取　　(　　　　　　　　　　　　　　　　　)

a. recent years
b. bad diet
c. sugar intake
d. drink company
e. personal choice

## D Reading Comprehension

**本文をよく読んで、正しければT、間違っていればFに○をつけましょう。**

1. The UK is the only country to introduce a sugar tax.　**(T / F)**
2. Everybody in the UK supports the sugar tax.　**(T / F)**

## E Read and Think

**第3パラグラフを読み、砂糖税によって期待されることをまとめてみましょう。**

① 企業は＿＿＿＿＿＿＿＿＿＿＿＿＿＿＿＿＿＿＿＿＿＿＿＿＿＿＿＿。

② 消費者は＿＿＿＿＿＿＿＿＿＿＿＿＿＿＿＿＿＿＿＿＿＿＿＿＿＿＿。

③ 政府は悪い食習慣によって起きる糖尿病、肥満、虫歯やその他の問題に取り組むために砂糖税を費やすことができる。

## F Useful Expressions（may or may not）

**下線部に注意して、和訳しましょう。**

1. The sugar tax may or may not be the solution.

2. I may or may not go on a diet in the New Year—I haven’t decided yet.

## G Over to You

**あなたは日本でも sugar tax が必要だと思いますか？　その理由を含めて、考えてみましょう。**

### Tea Break

**「食」について考える映画 Culinary Cinema—『あまくない砂糖の話』**

オーストラリア映画『あまくない砂糖の話』（That Sugar Film　2014）は、60 日間 1 日小さじ 40 杯の砂糖を摂取するドキュメンタリーです。私たちがふだん、何気なく食べている食品の中にどれだけの砂糖が含まれているかを考える良いきっかけになります。

米を主食とし、子供のころから食育が進んでいる日本とオーストラリアを簡単に比較することは危険ですが、自分がふだん食べているものについて考えるきっかけを与えてくれる良い映画です。

# UNIT 14 抗酸化物質 Antioxidants

## 考えてみましょう

テレビや雑誌では体に良い食品について特集をすることがよくありますが、あなたは、どういった食品が健康に良いと思いますか？　具体的な食品の名前を挙げてみましょう。

〈メモ〉

The key to staying young

## A Vocabulary Check 41

次の日本語の意味を表す英語を下の語群から選び、(　　　) 内に書き出しなさい。また、音声を聴いてそれぞれの単語を発音しなさい。

1. 酸化 (　　　　　　　　　　　　　　　　　　　)
2. 県 (　　　　　　　　　　　　　　　　　　　)
3. 含む (　　　　　　　　　　　　　　　　　　　)
4. 酸素 (　　　　　　　　　　　　　　　　　　　)
5. 物質 (　　　　　　　　　　　　　　　　　　　)

**語群**

substance　oxygen　prefecture　contain　oxidation

## B Dictation 42

次の英文を聴き、______ に適切な語句を記入しなさい。

We [1] ____________ and feel older, and our [2] ____________ actually get older. Oxidation in the [3] ____________ body is made worse by stress, [4] ____________, pollution, and other factors [5] ____________ to the body.

## Reading Passage 43

[1] Today, people want to be more in control of their diet and eat healthily. So, you often hear buzzwords such as "superfood" (see Unit 8), "organic," "gluten-free," and so on. Another word you hear these days is "antioxidant."

[2] To understand this, you must first know about oxidation. When oxygen combines with another substance, it changes that substance and creates something new; this is called oxidation. A good example of this is when iron goes rusty—this is a result of oxidation. When oxidation happens in our body, it speeds up the aging process. So, we look and feel older, and our bodies actually get older. Oxidation in the human body is made worse by stress, smoking, pollution, and other factors harmful to the body.

[3] However, antioxidants can help. Food or ingredients with antioxidants will help fight against oxidation and the body's aging process. Such foods tend to be high in antioxidants, including vitamins A, C, E and other useful minerals such as lutein and selenium. The most common antioxidant foods are fruits and vegetables, especially brightly colored ones; pomegranates, broccoli, and eggplant are all high in antioxidants. Also, nuts, dark chocolate, and green tea all contain ingredients with antioxidant effects. In fact, in Japan, the number of deaths caused by cancer is lowest in places that produce green tea, such as Kakegawa and Hamamatsu in Shizuoka Prefecture and Tokorozawa in Saitama Prefecture.

[4] No one can live forever. However, if you want to stay young, antioxidants could be the key.

(249 words)

| | | | |
|---|---|---|---|
| Speed Reading | 1st time | ( | /wpm) |
| Speed Reading | 2nd time | ( | /wpm) |

## C Scan the Text

**1-5 の日本語の語句と同じ意味の英語の表現を a-e から選び、(　　　　) に記入しましょう。また、本文をよく読み、それらの表現に下線を引きましょう。**

1. 健康的に食べる　(　　　　　　　　　　)
2. 老化　(　　　　　　　　　　)
3. さびる　(　　　　　　　　　　)
4. 抗酸化物質を含む食品や食材　(　　　　　　　　　　)
5. はやり言葉　(　　　　　　　　　　)

a　the aging process
b.　buzzword
c.　go rusty
d.　food or ingredients with antioxidants
e.　eat healthily

## D Reading Comprehension

**本文をよく読んで、正しければ T、間違っていれば F に○をつけましょう。**

1. Consuming dark chocolate speeds up the aging process.　(T / F)
2. As a healthy eating habit, we should avoid antioxidants.　(T / F)

## E Read and Think

**本文をよく読んで、抗酸化作用のある食品を書き出しましょう。**

------------------------------------------------------------

------------------------------------------------------------

------------------------------------------------------------

## F *Useful Expressions*（such as, and so on）

**下線部に注意して、和訳しましょう。**

1. You often hear buzzwords such as “superfood,” “organic,” “gluten-free,” and so on.

------------------------------------------------------------

2. Recently, I’ve been eating more healthy food, such as fruits, vegetables, nuts, and so on.

------------------------------------------------------------

## G *Over to You*

**抗酸化物質を含む食品を食生活に取り入れるためにどんなことを心がけたらよいでしょうか？考えてみましょう。**

------------------------------------------------------------

------------------------------------------------------------

------------------------------------------------------------

------------------------------------------------------------

------------------------------------------------------------

### Tea Break

**知っていますか？**

クイズ：ほうれん草に豊富な鉄の吸収を高める食べ物はどれでしょうか？
2つ、選びましょう。

A　キウイフルーツ
B　椎茸
C　豚肉

UNIT 15

# 遺伝子組み換え食品

# Genetically Modified Food

## 考えてみましょう

あなたは、食品を買うとき、遺伝子組み換え食品について、意識したことがありますか？

〈メモ〉

GM food everywhere

## A Vocabulary Check 44

**次の日本語の意味を表す英語を下の語群から選び、(　　　) 内に書き出しなさい。また、音声を聴いてそれぞれの単語を発音しなさい。**

1. 殺虫剤 (　　　　　　　　　　　　　　　)
2. 農作物 (　　　　　　　　　　　　　　　)
3. 雑草 (　　　　　　　　　　　　　　　)
4. 心配事 (　　　　　　　　　　　　　　　)
5. 有機体 (　　　　　　　　　　　　　　　)

語群

weed　crop　pesticide　organism　worry

## B Dictation 45

**次の英文を聴き、＿＿＿＿に適切な語句を記入しなさい。**

Humans have [1] ____________ tried to make farming methods more [2] ____________ and efficient. One [3] ____________ example of this is genetically modified (GM) food. GM food comes from a genetically modified organism (GMO)—an organism in which genetic material (DNA) is deliberately [4] ____________ from its [5] ____________ form.

# Reading Passage 46

[1] Humans have always tried to make farming methods more productive and efficient. One modern example of this is genetically modified (GM) food. GM food comes from a genetically modified organism (GMO)—an organism in which genetic material (DNA) is deliberately changed from its original form. Some common GM foods that we find in the supermarket are corn, canola, potatoes, and soybeans.

[2] Many believe that GMOs have a positive impact on our lives. They are created so that crops are stronger against diseases and can survive through severe weather conditions. This also means that it is possible to make crops available using fewer pesticides. Furthermore, some GMOs are designed to improve taste as well as increase nutritional value. In certain cases, they even lead to development of new medicine.

[3] However, not everybody supports GM food. One big concern is health; some studies have found that animals fed on GM crops suffer more serious diseases and live shorter than animals fed on regular crops. Another worry is the environmental impact; the GM process makes crops stronger, but it can also make weeds stronger. As a result, farmers use more pesticides to treat this ‘superweed,’ killing not only the weed but also other natural organisms such as insects and plants. The environmental damage from this is serious.

[4] Japan is said to be more cautious about GM products, but many products consumed in Japan come from overseas, where regulations are different. So, if you are concerned about possible GMOs in your diet, it’s important to always check the label and try to learn more about how your food was produced.

(266 words)

| | | |
|---|---|---|
| Speed Reading | 1st time ( | /wpm) |
| Speed Reading | 2nd time ( | /wpm) |

**NOTES**

**Canola** キャノーラ、菜種の遺伝子操作による変種

## C Scan the Text

**1-5 の日本語の語句と同じ意味の英語の表現を a-e から選び、(　　　　) に記入しましょう。また、本文をよく読み、それらの表現に下線を引きましょう。**

1. 良い影響　(　　　　　　　　　　　　　　)
2. 厳しい気象条件　(　　　　　　　　　　　　　　)
3. 栄養価　(　　　　　　　　　　　　　　)
4. 新しい医薬品の開発　(　　　　　　　　　　　　　　)
5. 大きな懸念事項　(　　　　　　　　　　　　　　)

a. severe weather conditions
b. nutritional value
c. development of new medicine
d. big concern
e. positive impact

## D Reading Comprehension

**本文をよく読んで、正しければ T、間違っていれば F に○をつけましょう。**

1. In Japan, GM food has never been imported. **(T / F)**
2. The regulations about GM food are universal. **(T / F)**

## E Read and Think

**第 3 パラグラフを読み、遺伝子組み換え食品について、どちらがあてはまるか、○をつけてみましょう。**

ある研究によると、遺伝子組み換え食品を飼料としている動物は深刻な病気に（①なりにくく・なりやすく）、寿命が（②長い・短い）。また、遺伝子組み換えの過程により、作物は（③強く・弱く）なるが、それとともに雑草も（④強く・弱く）なり、使われる多量の農薬によって他の有機体に害を及ぼしている。

## F *Useful Expressions*（be said to be）

**下線部に注意して、和訳しましょう。**

1. Japan is said to be more cautious about GM products.

------------------------------------------------------------

2. Japanese school lunches are said to be healthier than those in many other countries.

------------------------------------------------------------

## G *Over to You*

**海外から食品を輸入することの良い点、悪い点をまとめてみましょう。**

------------------------------------------------------------

------------------------------------------------------------

------------------------------------------------------------

------------------------------------------------------------

------------------------------------------------------------

### Tea Break

**「食」について考える映画 Culinary Cinema―『パパ、遺伝子組み換えってなぁに？』**

本文にあるように、現在のところは、日本は遺伝子組み換え作物について慎重な態度を取っていると考えられています。海外の事情はどうなっているのでしょうか？

『パパ、遺伝子組み換えってなぁに？』（GMO OMG　2013）では、子育て中のお父さんが、遺伝子組み換え作物に興味を持ち、世界各地を取材して巡るロードムービーです。遺伝子組み換え作物が危険なのか、安全なのか、まだわかっていませんが、自分の食べているものはどこからきて、どのように作られているのかを考えさせられるでしょう。

## Speed Reading (wpm) Record Sheet

| Unit | 1st time | | 2nd time | | 3rd time | | 4th time | |
|---|---|---|---|---|---|---|---|---|
| | date | wpm | date | wpm | date | wpm | date | wpm |
| 1 | | | | | | | | |
| 2 | | | | | | | | |
| 3 | | | | | | | | |
| 4 | | | | | | | | |
| 5 | | | | | | | | |
| 6 | | | | | | | | |
| 7 | | | | | | | | |
| 8 | | | | | | | | |
| 9 | | | | | | | | |
| 10 | | | | | | | | |
| 11 | | | | | | | | |
| 12 | | | | | | | | |
| 13 | | | | | | | | |
| 14 | | | | | | | | |
| 15 | | | | | | | | |

*MEMO*

## Shadowing/Reading Aloud Record Sheet

| Unit | 1st time | | 2nd time | | 3rd time | |
|---|---|---|---|---|---|---|
| | **Shadowing** | **R/Aloud** | **Shadowing** | **R/Aloud** | **Shadowing** | **R/Aloud** |
| 1 | | | | | | |
| 2 | | | | | | |
| 3 | | | | | | |
| 4 | | | | | | |
| 5 | | | | | | |
| 6 | | | | | | |
| 7 | | | | | | |
| 8 | | | | | | |
| 9 | | | | | | |
| 10 | | | | | | |
| 11 | | | | | | |
| 12 | | | | | | |
| 13 | | | | | | |
| 14 | | | | | | |
| 15 | | | | | | |

日付を記入しましょう。

*MEMO*

# *A Matter of Taste* 〈Intro〉

[B-896]

## 健康生活に見る食育と栄養〈入門編〉

第 1 刷　2020 年 4 月 1 日

著　者　津田　晶子　Akiko Tsuda
クリストファー・ヴァルヴォーナ　Chris Valvona
大和　孝子　Takako Yamato
ヴァルヴォーナ　綾乃　Ayano Valvona
英文校閲　ケリー・マクドナルド　Kelly MacDonald

発行者　南雲一範　Kazunori Nagumo
発行所　株式会社　南雲堂
〒162-0801　東京都新宿区山吹町361
NAN'UN-DO Publishing Co., Ltd.
361 Yamabuki-cho, Shinjuku-ku, Tokyo 162-0801, Japan
振替口座：00160-0-46863
TEL:　03-3268-2311（営業部：学校関係）
03-3268-2384（営業部：書店関係）
03-3268-2387（編集部）
FAX:　03-3269-2486

編集者　丸小雅臣／伊藤宏実
組版・印刷　啓文堂
装　丁　N スタジオ
検　印　省　略
コード　ISBN978-4-523-17896-5 C0082

Printed in Japan



E-mail　nanundo@post.email.ne.jp
URL　https://www.nanun-do.co.jp/